Garfield

Why do you hate Mondays?

JIM DAVIS

ℛℛ

Ravette London

This edition first published by
Ravette Limited 1982
Reprinted 1983, 1984, 1985, 1986 (twice),
1987 (twice)

Printed and bound in Great Britain
for Ravette Limited,
3 Glenside Estate, Star Road, Partridge Green,
Horsham, Sussex RH13 8RA
by Cox & Wyman Ltd, Reading

ISBN 0 906710 07 3

© 1982 United Feature Syndicate, Inc.   2-22

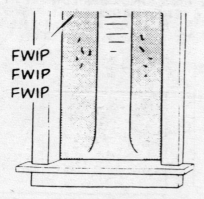

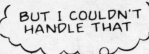

© 1981 United Feature Syndicate, Inc

SWIPE!

I HATE MONDAYS

© 1981 United Feature Syndicate, Inc.

PUNT

© 1982 United Feature Syndicate, Inc.

ROWR!

4·29

JIM DAVIS

© 1981 United Feature Syndicate, Inc.

OKAY, GARFIELD. ONE BITE

© 1982 United Feature Syndicate, Inc.

2-26

SMACK!
SLURP!

JIM DAVIS   3-5

YOU HAVE THE MANNERS
OF A PIG, GARFIELD.
SLOW DOWN AND
SPIT OUT THE SEEDS

RATA TATA
TATA TATA

© 1982 United Feature Syndicate, Inc.

OBOY! MY FEET CAN TOUCH THE FLOOR AGAIN!

JIM DAVIS 2-20

© 1982 United Feature Syndicate, Inc.

GARFIELD, GARFIELD GARFIELD

JIM DAVIS

1-4-82

© 1981 United Feature Syndicate, Inc.

JIM DAVIS

© 1981 United Feature Syndicate, Inc.

SHOOP!

7-15

BASH!

© 1981 United Feature Syndicate, Inc

7-16

GOOD MORNING, FATSO

ALL I DID WAS JUMP OFF THE BED

IT ISN'T HEALTHY FOR A CAT TO BE AS BIG AS YOU ARE, GARFIELD

JIM DAVIS   7-17

WHY, YOU COULD GET HEART DISEASE, GET FALLEN ARCHES...

GET HARPOONED

COULDN'T RESIST IT COULD YOU

© 1981 United Feature Syndicate Inc

CRASH

7-14

© 1981 United Feature Syndicate, Inc

JIM DAVIS

© 1981 United Feature Syndicate, Inc.

7-13

JIM DAVIS 5·2

GOBBLE GOBBLE
GOBBLE GOBBLE

GARFIELD

IT'S BEEN A BIG DAY

© 1981 United Feature Syndicate, Inc.

© 1982 United Feature Syndicate, Inc.

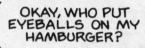

OKAY, WHO PUT EYEBALLS ON MY HAMBURGER?

5-9

JIM DAVIS

1-15

BUT YOU HAVE MORE CHINS
THAN A HONG KONG
TELEPHONE DIRECTORY!

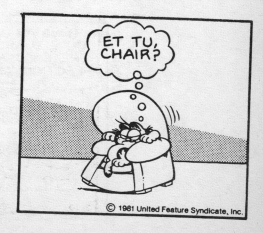

AUNT GUSSIE, WOULD YOU TAKE CARE OF MY CAT WHILE I'M GONE ON VACATION? ...TERRIFIC!

JIM DAVIS

YOU KNOW AUNT GUSSIE, GARFIELD. SHE'S A SWEET OLD LADY

8-13

HOW CAN YOU SAY THAT ABOUT SOMEONE WHO USED TO DOUBLE DATE WITH LIZZIE BORDEN?

WHILE I'M GONE TAKE GOOD CARE OF GARFIELD

JIM DAVIS

AND KEEP A CLOSE EYE ON HIM. HE GETS INTO A LOT OF MISCHIEF

8-15

HAVE FUN, GARFIELD

GARFIELD?

© 1981 United Feature Syndicate

8-22

1-22 © 1981 United Feature Syndicate, Inc

1-23

WE GOTTA BUST OUT OF THIS POUND. GOT ANY IDEAS?

WHY DON'T WE USE FLUFFY AS A BATTERING RAM?

1-20

FLUFFY! BE A BATTERING RAM!

YAH

CRASH!

CRUNCH

JIM DAVIS

3-2

CRUNCH
CRUNCH
CRUNCH

THAT FROZEN PIZZA WOULD BE MUCH BETTER IF YOU BAKED IT FIRST

© 1982 United Feature Syndicate, Inc.

WHAT'S SO SPECIAL ABOUT A PET-OWNER RELATIONSHIP, GARFIELD?

COULD IT BE EVERYONE NEEDS SOMEONE TO LORD OVER?

COULD BE

© 1981 United Feature Syndicate, Inc.   JIM DAVIS

BUT WHAT DO **YOU** GET OUT OF IT?

11-13

JIM DAVIS

3-15

© 1982 United Feature Syndicate, Inc.

5-12

2-13 JIM DAVIS

SORRY ABOUT THAT

© 1981 United Feature Syndicate, Inc.

OTHER GARFIELD BOOKS IN THIS SERIES

LANDSCAPE SERIES

TV SPECIALS

Here Comes Garfield	£2.95
Garfield On The Town	£2.95
Garfield In The Rough	£2.95
Garfield In Disguise	£2.95
Garfield In Paradise	£2.95

All these books are available at your local bookshop or newsagent, or can be ordered direct from the publisher. Just tick the titles you require and fill in the form below. Prices and availability subject to change without notice.

Ravette Limited, 3 Glenside Estate, Star Road, Partridge Green, Horsham, West Sussex RH13 8RA

Please send a cheque or postal order, and allow the following for postage and packing. UK: Pocket-books and TV Specials – 45p for one book plus 20p for the second book and 15p for each additional book. Landscape Series – 45p for one book plus 30p for each additional book.

Name ....

Address ....

....